A selection of my skills

Name _____ Class _____

From the panel on the right, choose the correct word to write in each of these sentences about yourself.

1 I am a _____ at this school.

2 I am wearing _____ and _____ on my feet.

3 This is Book _____ in a _____ of eight.

4 I can _____ with a rope.

5 I know how to set up the nine pins for a game of _____.

6 I am good at _____.

7 I wash my hands and face with _____ and water.

   For my hair I use a _____.

8 I can recognise the _____ of the school bell, footsteps and the ticking of a clock.

9 I can recognise the _____ of oranges, paraffin and onions.

10 I know how to use a pair of _____.

11 I know that a _____ is a _____ with four equal sides and four right angles.

12 I know the address of our doctor's _____.

13 I know a church with a _____.

14 I know when milk is _____.

15 I can recognise these birds:— _____

    _____

16 I know how to keep a _____. I never tell it to anyone.

17 I can tell a _____ from a _____ by his uniform.

18 I know how to tell the time on a _____

19 I know that _____ is directly opposite north.

20 I know the price of a first-class _____ for a letter.

This is my _____.

sailor
sandals
scholar
scissors
sea-gull
secret
series
seven
shampoo
shape
shoes
signature
skip
skittles
skylark
slippers
smell
soap
socks
soldier
sound
sour
south
sparrow
spire
sports
square
stamp
starling
stockings
sundial
surgery
swallow
swan

Damage has been done

The pictures show that some damage has been done to each object.
Write two sentences about each picture.

A Choose the best word from this list to use in a sentence describing what has happened.

bent	broken	decayed	scratched	tangled	wilted
blunted	burst	injured	split	torn	wrecked

B Choose the best word from this list to use in a sentence describing how to repair the damage

bound	filled	recovered	sealed	stitched	unravelled
dressed	glazed	resprayed	sharpened	straightened	watered

The first one has been done for you.

1 *The shirt has been torn. It will have to be stitched.*

2

3

4

5

6

7

8

9

10

11

12

Adjectives

A From the adjectives in **Panel C**, tick ✓ the one which has the
as the **adjective** printed in the first list.
Write it in Column **A**.

B From the adjectives in **Panel D**, tick ✓ the one which means the **opposite** of
the adjective in the first list .
Write it in Column **B**.
The first one is done for you.

	Adjective	A Same meaning	B Opposite		Panel C	Panel D
1	bashful	*shy*	*bold*		annoyed	bold ✓
2	brave				bitter	busy
3	broad				cold	certain
4	calm				common	cheap
5	cheeky				courageous	clear
6	chilly				dangerous	cowardly
7	costly				dim	cruel
8	crazy				exhausted	false
9	cross				expensive	fancy
10	doubtful				gentle	light
11	dull				huge	narrow
12	enormous				impudent	noisy
13	fresh				lasting	pleased
14	genuine				lazy	polite
15	heavy				mad	refreshed
16	idle				new	safe
17	loose				peaceful	sensible
18	neat				real	stale
19	ordinary				shy ✓	sweet
20	perilous				simple	tight
21	permanent				slack	tiny
22	plain				tidy	untidy
23	sour				undecided	unusual
24	tender				weighty	temporary
25	weary				wide	warm

Reading a map

Crossroads at sea—the Strait of Dover

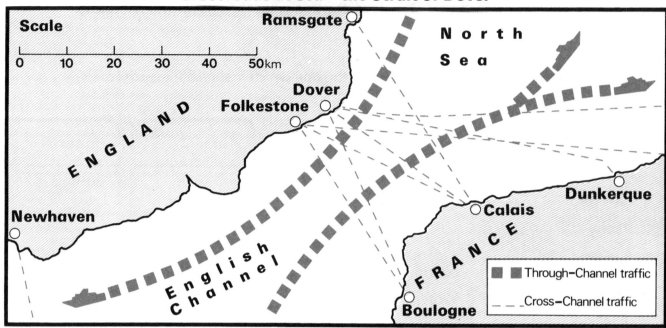

This is a map of the **Strait of Dover**. It shows the routes taken by ships sailing through, or across it.

The Strait of Dover is one of the world's most crowded shipping lanes. During one day, in summer, there can be as many as three hundred and fifty ships passing through the Strait, and over two hundred ships crossing the Strait.

There are strict international rules as to which route a ship must follow.

Study the map and write **sentences** in answer to these questions.

1 Why are there strict rules for traffic in the Strait of Dover?

2 Are these rules only for ships registered in Britain or France?

3 Nearer which coast must traffic **from** the North Sea keep?

4 Nearer which coast must traffic travelling **to** the North Sea keep?

5 Which is the busiest English port shown on the map, and to which French ports are cross-Channel ships travelling from there?

6 Which is the busiest French port shown on the map, and to which English ports are cross-Channel ships travelling from there?

7 Between which two ports shown on the map is the shortest cross-Channel route? How long is it?

8 In what kind of weather is the Strait of Dover most dangerous for shipping?

_____.

9 What equipment must a ship have to show the captain the position of other ships?

_____.

10 The captain of a ship has to be alert to other dangers than sea-traffic.
Five of these dangers are here in mixed letters. Write each one correctly in the space.

a lesag_____ **b** korcs _____ **c** banskdans _____

d detis _____ **e** kscerw _____

11

M	— —
N	— .
O	— — —
P	. — — .
Q	— — . —
R	. — .
S	. . .

This is part of the Morse Code once commonly used for signalling by lamp or radio.

Write, in Morse Code, the international distress call signalled when a ship was in great danger.

12 Another distress signal, passed by radio-telephone from a ship or an aircraft, was from the French "M'AIDEZ", meaning "HELP ME".

Write this distress signal, **as it sounds**, in English. _____

13 Each of these is ready to help a ship, should the need arise.

> coastguard   helicopter   lifeboat   lightship

Choose the correct word, from the four, to write in each of these sentences.

a A_____ is a vessel specially designed for saving shipwrecked people.

b The _____ records each ship as it passes his station.

c With its beacon, a _____ guides or warns ships and aircraft.

d A_____ is a flying-machine which can hover above a ship.

14 Here are drawings of five vessels which may be seen, at some time, in the Strait of Dover. They are a **car ferry**, a **frigate**, a **hovercraft**, a **tanker** and a **trawler**. Choose the correct name to write under each drawing.

1_____ 2_____ 3_____ 4_____ 5_____

Which of these vessels are most likely to be **crossing** the English Channel?

_____

Which of these vessels are most likely to be **sailing through** the English Channel?

_____

Pronouns

A pronoun is a word used instead of a noun.

For example,   The man had great fun with the old camera.
              First of all, **he** took **it** to pieces.

The pronoun **he** is used instead of **The man**.
The pronoun **it** is used instead of **the old camera**.

I	we	he	she	you	they	it	these
me	us	him	her	your	them	its	those
mine	our	his	hers	yours	their		
my	ours				theirs		

A From this list of pronouns choose the correct ones to write in these sentences.

1 "My Mum is going to buy _____ some new shoes. _____ are too small

   for _____."

2 Susan closed _____ eyes at bedtime. _____ did not open _____ until dawn.

3 Alan searched all _____ pockets for the coin.

4 The dancing instructor said to Karen, "_____ must put _____ left hand on

   _____ right shoulder, and _____ right hand in _____ left hand."

5 John did well today. _____ passed _____ badge-test. Dad will buy _____

   the badge, and Mum will bake _____ one of _____ 'specials'.

6 "The books are all mixed up. Please put _____ on this shelf here,

   and _____ on that shelf over there."

7 "When _____ rang up the dentist, _____ said _____ could fit

   both of _____ in at two o'clock."

8 "There's a dog in the field, David. Is it _____?" asked the teacher.

   "No, it's not _____," said David. "The twins have one like that.

   Perhaps it is _____. _____ will ask _____."

9 _____ will put the hamster back into _____ cage. _____ seems to be

   afraid of _____.

10 Crossfield School are coming to play _____ school on Thursday.
    Crossfield should win as _____ team is better than _____.

B The person who wrote the following did not know about pronouns.

The shopkeeper said to Dora Dockett, "The shopkeeper wonders if Dora Dockett
knows Susan Sampson. If so, will Dora Dockett please tell Susan Sampson that the
shopkeeper has Susan Sampson's purse here?. Susan Sampson left the purse on the
shopkeeper's counter when Susan Sampson was here earlier this morning."

Rewrite this using **pronouns** in the most suitable places.

_____

_____

_____

_____

_____

_____

Helpful animals

Many animals are helpful to man.

Complete these sentences which describe the pictures.
Write in the name of the animal and choose a verb from this list.

carrying	controlling	giving	guiding	pulling
catching	eating	guarding	hauling	searching

The first one is done for you.

1 A _horse_ is _carrying_ a cowboy.

2 A_____ is _____ a blind man.

3 A_____ is _____ harmful insects.

4 A_____ is _____ a building.

5 Two_____ are _____ a plough.

6 A_____ is _____ a mouse.

7 An_____ is _____ a tree trunk.

8 Eight_____ are _____ a sledge.

9 A_____ is_____ a basket of fruit

10 A_____ is _____ a bale of cotton.

11 A_____ is _____ a flock of sheep.

12 A_____ is _____ for rabbits.

13 Two_____ are _____ a load of barrels.

14 A_____ is _____ its fleece for wool.

15 A_____ is _____ milk.

Black and white

You will hear or read a number of words or phrases containing the words **black** or **white**.

A

> sudden fainting or collapse
>
> a plague epidemic in 1348
>
> one who has brought disgrace on the family
>
> coal
>
> a punishment cell like that in India in 1756
>
> a record of the names of people who have been warned
>
> a prison van
>
> a bruised part of the face
>
> a package of recording equipment put into an aircraft
>
> an industrial district in the Midlands

From this list of meanings choose the correct one to write after each of these words or phrases.

1 a black box _____
2 the Black Country _____
3 the Black Death _____
4 black diamonds _____
5 a black eye _____
6 the Black Hole of Calcutta _____
7 a black list _____
8 a Black Maria _____
9 a blackout _____
10 a black sheep _____

B

> a well-meant phrase which is not strictly true
>
> a liquid used for coating walls
>
> the fluid surrounding the yolk
>
> a substitute for turpentine
>
> one who works as a clerk or does no manual labour
>
> white-crested waves at sea
>
> pale with fear or illness
>
> a sign of truce or surrender
>
> the residence of the President of the United States of America
>
> anything that gives more trouble than it is worth

From this list of meanings, choose the correct one to write after each of these words or phrases.

1 a white-collar worker _____
2 a white elephant _____
3 white-faced _____
4 a white flag _____
5 white horses _____
6 the White House _____
7 a white lie _____
8 white spirit _____
9 whitewash _____
10 the white of an egg _____

A If the word **m e a t** written in code is **W X Y Z**, what word does each of these code words stand for?

1 W X _____

4 Y Z _____

7 X Y Z _____

2 W Y Z _____

5 W X Z _____

8 Z Y W X _____

3 Z X Y W _____

6 W Y Z X _____

B

1 If **Q X K J V** stands for **h o r s e**, what does Q V K X stand for?

_____

2 If **P Y B G D F** stands for **n a t u r e**, what does B G P F stand for?

_____

3 If **M W H K S** stands for **t a b l e**, what does H K S W M stand for?

_____

4 If **X R D B L** stands for **p e a c h**, what does B L R D X stand for?

_____

5 If **Z M J U V** stands for **s a i n t**, what does V J U Z stand for?

_____

C Here are four words **e a s t   m a s t   s e a t   e a t s**

Below, the same words are put in code in a different order. The code is the same all through.

Find the right word for each code word, and write it after the code word.

_____

_____

_____

_____

D Find the message hidden in this line of printing.

ameetbcmedeftonightghijatklmnosixpqrstu

_____

E This is a message printed in a simple code. Can you decipher it?

ESAELP   ETIRW   RUOY   SDROW   SDRAWKCAB

_____

Words with ph

A Under each picture, complete the name which must have **ph** (sounding like **f**) in it.

aut	cen	el	geog
g	meg	mic	ne
tom	acy	ant	oto
sax	si	nx	t

---

hyphen	orphan	paragraph	prophet	typhoon

B Write each of these words before its correct meaning.

_____ — one who foretells future events

_____ — someone who has lost both parents

_____ — a violent storm

_____ — a short dash between two words

_____ — a short written passage or collection of sentences

Verbs

Some verbs can have two, or more, meanings depending on the way in which they are used.
For example,   You can **stamp** a letter   *or*   you can **stamp** your feet.
You can **grow** very angry   *or*   you can **grow** some lettuce.

address	bolt	forge	pass	raise	stop
admit	comb	head	pick	rule	thread
bank	cut	join	pitch	settle	wait
beat	draw	keep	poach	stand	weigh

From this list of verbs choose the one to use twice in each of these sentences.

1 You can _____ a drum or you can _____ another player.

2 You can _____ a secret or you can _____ guinea-pigs.

3 You can _____ your hair or you can _____ the beach for driftwood.

4 You can _____ an examination or you can _____ a slow walker.

5 You can _____ a straight line or you can _____ a country.

6 You can _____ a parcel on the scales or you can _____ anchor.

7 You can _____ your hands above your head or you can _____ a family.

8 You can _____ your finger or you can _____ a pack of cards.

9 You can _____ an egg or you can _____ the keeper's pheasants.

10 You can _____ money or you can _____ an aircraft.

11 You can _____ two pieces of wire or you can _____ a club.

12 You can _____ an envelope or you can _____ a meeting.

13 You can _____ a football or you can _____ a procession.

14 You can _____ a signature or you can _____ some iron.

15 You can _____ the winning horse or you can _____ some flowers.

16 You can _____ a door or you can _____ a meal.

17 You can _____ a picture or you can _____ your Post Office savings.

18 You can _____ on your own two feet or you can _____ pain.

19 You can _____ at a bus-stop or you can _____ at table.

20 You can _____ that noise or you can _____ for a day or two with us.

21 You can _____ a visitor to your home or you can _____ a mistake.

22 You can _____ a tent or you can _____ a quoit.

23 You can _____ a bill or you can _____ in comfort in an easy chair.

24 You can _____ a needle or you can _____ your way through a crowd.

Occupations

architect	fireman	librarian	photographer	umpire
builder	gardener	milkman	quarryman	vet
chemist	hairdresser	musician	shepherd	waitress
doctor	inventor	nurse	teacher	
engineer	judge	optician	tailor	

From this list, write in the numbered space the occupation suggested by each picture.

1 _____

2 _____

3 _____

4 _____

5 _____

6 _____

7 _____

8 _____

9 _____

10 _____

11 _____

12 _____

13 _____

14 _____

15 _____

16 _____

17 _____

18 _____

19 _____

20 _____

21 _____

22 _____

23 _____

Occupations

(A) From the list on page 12, choose the correct occupation to write in each of these sentences.

(B) From the panel on the right, choose the correct word to write at the end of each sentence to show where the occupation is carried out. Some words may be used more than once. The first sentence is completed for you.

1 A _____judge_____ tries and hears cases in a _____court_____.

2 A _____ reports events from a TV _____.

3 A _____ constructs a building on a _____.

4 A _____ answers a fire-alarm at his _____.

5 A _____ teaches a lesson in a _____.

6 A _____ treats sick animals in a _____.

7 A _____ is in charge of books in a _____.

8 A _____ prepares medicines in a _____.

9 An _____ sells spectacles in a _____.

10 A _____ serves meals in a _____.

11 A _____ dresses and cuts hair in a _____.

12 An _____ draws plans of buildings in an _____.

13 A _____ takes stone from the earth in a _____.

14 A _____ treats sick people in a _____.

15 An _____ controls a game of cricket on the _____.

16 A _____ plays with an orchestra in a _____.

17 An _____ attends to machinery in a _____.

18 A _____ tends his flock in the _____.

19 A _____ delivers milk from a _____.

20 A _____ uses a word processor in an _____.

21 A _____ grows vegetables on a _____.

22 A _____ takes pictures in a _____.

23 An _____ creates something new in a _____.

café
class-room
court
dairy
dispensary
factory
fields
hall
library
office
pitch
plot
quarry
salon
shop
site
station
studio
surgery
workshop

Group words

The words in each of the groups below are alike in some way but different from the words in the other groups.

Occupations

athlete	gymnast	matron	ploughman	shepherd
burglar	hurdler	midwife	reporter	shop-lifter
editor	journalist	nurseryman	robber	surgeon

From this list, write each word in its correct group below the two already there.

Group 1	Group 2	Group 3	Group 4	Group 5
author	thief	footballer	farmer	doctor
writer	criminal	cricketer	gardener	nurse
_____	_____	_____	_____	_____
_____	_____	_____	_____	_____
_____	_____	_____	_____	_____

B
Growing things

ash	daffodil	larch	pink	skylark
beech	haddock	mackerel	plaice	snowdrop
cheetah	hawk	owl	poplar	sparrow
cod	jaguar	pansy	puma	tiger

From this list, write each word in its correct group below the one already there.

Group 1	Group 2	Group 3	Group 4	Group 5
oak	rose	eagle	herring	lion
_____	_____	_____	_____	_____
_____	_____	_____	_____	_____
_____	_____	_____	_____	_____
_____	_____	_____	_____	_____

C Special people

In this list of people who, at some time, may be at your home, there are fifteen who belong to one special group.

acquaintance	cousin	guest	neighbour	teacher
aunt	daughter	husband	nephew	tenant
brother	employer	landlord	niece	traveller
caller	father	lodger	parents	uncle
cleaner	friend	milkman	sister	visitor
collector	grandson	mother	son	wife

Write the fifteen in the special group here.

_____	_____	_____	_____	_____
_____	_____	_____	_____	_____
_____	_____	_____	_____	_____

Apostrophe

This is an **apostrophe**   '

It looks like a comma written above a word.

One of its uses is to show that one or more letters have been missed out of the word.

For example,   **It's** means **It is**.   The apostrophe shows that the letter **i** has been missed out.

He'll means **He will**.   The letters **wi** have been missed out.

Write out each of these sentences in full.

1   He'd better look out.   _____

2   We'll come tomorrow.   _____

3   My watch isn't going.   _____

4   They can't find their way.   _____

5   I hope you'll soon be better.   _____

6   He wouldn't eat his breakfast.   _____

7   We've a long way to go yet.   _____

8   She's the winner.   _____

9   I think we're late for school.   _____

10   You've dropped your pencil.   _____

Put in the apostrophes which have been missed out of this letter.

Tomorrow it ll be Bonfire Night. We ve made a huge bonfire and there s a guy on top. He s made of old clothes. Dad says he d have helped us if he d had time. He ll be there tomorrow night. I ve saved up for the fireworks and Mum says she ll try and buy some more today. It s a law now that we re too young to buy them ourselves. Let s hope it s fine tomorrow night.

You will sometimes see shortened words in poetry where an apostrophe is used.

Write each of these words in full.

ne'er _____   o'er _____   'twas _____

'tween _____   'twill _____

This is part of a poem. Write all the words in full.

Where's the sun gone?   _____

Don't you know?   _____

It's slipped below the skyline,   _____

We're sure it had to go.   _____

P'r'aps tomorrow when you waken,   _____

You'll see it's here again.   _____

The History of England in ten periods

A time-chart showing dates and some important rulers together with their family names and the dates of their reigns.

Julius Caesar
55 B.C.–44 B.C.

Alfred the Great
871–899

William I
1066–1087

Elizabeth I
1558–1603

Charles II
1660–1685

| Roman | Anglo-Saxon | Norman | P L Y | Tudor | Stuart | C | Stuart |

| 55 B.C. | A.D. 455 | 1066 | 1154 1399 1461 1485 | 1603 | 1660 1685 | 1714 |

P = Plantaganet   L = Lancaster   Y = York   C = Commonwealth

Victoria
1837–1901

Edward VII
1901–1910

George V
1910–1936

George VI
1936–1952

Elizabeth II
1952–

| Hanover | Saxe-Coburg | Windsor |

| 1714 1830 1898 Boer 1901 | 1910 1914 World 1918 | 1939 World 1945 |
| War | War I | War II |

From the details of dates, rulers and events shown above, write sentences in answer to these questions.

1   If a century is one hundred years, how many centuries does this chart cover?

2   In which century are we now?

3   What do the abbreviations B.C. and A.D. mean?

4   Why is Queen Elizabeth, who succeeded her father in 1952, known as Elizabeth II?

5   How many King Georges has the United Kingdom had?

6   How many crowned Kings of England have been named Edward?

7   If the period from 1837 to 1901 is called the Victorian Period, what name is given to the Period from 1901 to 1910?

8   Who was on the throne of the United Kingdom when your grandparents were born?

9   Who was on the throne of the United Kingdom when your parents were born?

10   Everyone in Britain is expected to know 1066 as an important date. What happened on that date?

11 What was the family name of Queen Elizabeth I?

_____

12 People in Britain still emigrate to countries which used to be part of the British Empire. Name two of these countries.

_____

13 Who was Julius Caesar?

_____

How do we know that the Romans were once in Britain?

_____

14 A monarch is a sovereign or ruler with the title of King or Queen.
A Royal Jubilee is a special anniversary of the monarch's coming to the throne.
A Silver Jubilee celebrates twenty-five years, a Golden Jubilee fifty years
and a Diamond Jubilee sixty years.
From the details given on the chart, work out and write down the name of the
monarch and the jubilee celebrated on each of these dates.

1887 _____

1897 _____

1935 _____

1977 _____

15 The reign of Edward VII ended when he died at the age of sixty-eight.
In what year was he born?

_____

16 When older people talk about "The First War" what do they mean?

_____

17 Of all the kings and queens named on the chart, which one had the longest reign?

_____

18 On which everyday object are you likely to see this inscription
D·G·   REG·   F·D·   1988   ELIZABETH II?

_____

19 Each district has some important historical monument or building.
Describe one in your district.

_____

20 Sometimes, when an important public building is being erected, a number of
everyday articles are buried in a casket which is then bricked over.
Why is this done?

_____

Imagine such a building is to be erected in your district, and you are asked to find five articles
to be buried in the casket. All the articles must have the date on them.
Which five articles would you choose?

_____

_____

Analogies

Look at the first pair of words.
The second pair of words must match each other in the same way.

For example, **kitten** is to **cat** as **puppy** is to **dog**
eye is to **blind** as **ear** is to **deaf**

Write the last word in each of these. In the first ten the first letter is given.

1   **calf**   is to **cow**   as **lamb**   is to s_____
2   **father** is to **son**   as **mother** is to d_____
3   **aunt**   is to **uncle**   as **niece** is to n_____
4   **thirsty** is to **drink**   as **hungry** is to f_____
5   **smell**   is to **scent**   as **hear**   is to s_____
6   **tall**   is to **short**   as **fat**   is to t_____
7   **flock**   is to **sheep**   as **swarm** is to b_____
8   **hand**   is to **wrist**   as **foot**   is to a_____
9   **moon**   is to **night**   as **sun**   is to d_____
10 **rich**   is to **poor**   as **full**   is to e_____
11 **single** is to **one**   as **double** is to _____
12 **narrow** is to **wide**   as **short** is to _____
13 **meow**   is to **cat**   as **quack** is to _____
14 **early**   is to **late**   as **near**   is to _____
15 **cold**   is to **warm**   as **winter** is to _____
16 **bullet** is to **gun**   as **arrow** is to _____
17 **foot**   is to **shoe**   as **hand**   is to _____
18 **light**   is to **dark**   as **dawn**   is to _____
19 **feather** is to **bird**   as **scale** is to _____
20 **man**   is to **men**   as **mouse** is to _____
21 **tie**   is to **neck**   as **belt**   is to _____
22 **brush**   is to **sweep**   as **pen**   is to _____
23 **clump**   is to **trees**   as **bunch** is to _____
24 **happy**   is to **sad**   as **win**   is to _____
25 **nut**   is to **shell**   as **pea**   is to _____

Verbs and nouns

What happens and where?

Each of these sentences should tell what happens to something and where it happens.

To complete each sentence, choose the correct verb from **Panel A** and then the correct noun from **Panel B**. Tick ✓ the verb or noun, when you have used it.

The first one is done for you.

Panel A	Panel B
acted	bakery
baked	bank
branded	booking-office
brewed	brewery
cashed	building-site
erected	colliery
exhibited	docks
felled	forest
generated	gallery
groomed	garage
harvested ✓	garden
imprisoned	hospital
issued	jail
laid	mill
mined	nest
nursed	office
played	orchard ✓
repaired	pitch
served	power-station
sown	ranch
stored	reservoir
taught	restaurant
typed	school
unloaded	stable
woven	stage

1   Apples are _____*harvested*_____ in an _____*orchard.*_____.

2   Beer is _____ in a _____.

3   Bread is _____ in a _____.

4   Cars are _____ in a _____.

5   Carpets are _____ in a _____.

6   Cheques are _____ in a _____.

7   Coal is _____ at a _____.

8   Criminals are _____ in a _____.

9   Eggs are _____ in a _____.

10 Electricity is _____ in a _____.

11 Football is _____ on a _____.

12 Horses are _____ in a _____.

13 Letters are _____ in an _____.

14 Meals are _____ in a _____.

15 Paintings are _____ in a _____.

16 Patients are _____ in a _____.

17 A play is _____ on a _____.

18 Pupils are _____ in a _____.

19 Scaffolding is _____ on a _____.

20 Seed is _____ in a _____.

21 Ships are _____ at the _____.

22 Steers are _____ on a _____.

23 Tickets are _____ at the _____.

24 Trees are _____ in a _____.

25 Water is _____ in a _____.

Last to first

The **last three letters** of one word become the **first three letters** of the next word.

For example,   **astronaut ⟶ autograph**

Writing one letter in each square, complete each of these words.

1

g ☐ ☐ ☐ ☐ ☐   ☐ ☐ ☐   ☐ ☐ ☐ ☐ ☐

2

f ☐ ☐ ☐ ☐ ☐ ☐   ☐ ☐ ☐ ☐ ☐ ☐ ☐ ☐ ☐   ☐ ☐ ☐ ☐ ☐ ☐

3

s ☐ ☐ ☐ ☐ ☐   ☐ ☐ ☐ ☐ ☐ ☐ ☐   ☐ ☐ ☐ ☐ ☐

4

p ☐ ☐ ☐ ☐ ☐   ☐ ☐ ☐ ☐ ☐ ☐ ☐   ☐ ☐ ☐ ☐ ☐ ☐

5

s ☐ ☐ ☐ ☐   ☐ ☐ ☐ ☐ ☐ ☐   ☐ ☐ ☐ ☐ ☐

6

o ☐ ☐ ☐ ☐   ☐ ☐ ☐ ☐   ☐ ☐ ☐ ☐ ☐

7

p ☐ ☐ ☐ ☐   ☐ ☐ ☐ ☐ ☐ ☐ ☐   ☐ ☐ ☐ ☐

8

c ☐ ☐ ☐ ☐   ☐ ☐ ☐ ☐   ☐ ☐ ☐ ☐ ☐ ☐

Word meanings

A Here are ten nouns.

antic	dairy	fir	foul	guard
antique	diary	fur	fowl	guide

Write each of these nouns in front of its meaning, as given here.

_____ — a cone-bearing tree

_____ — an object which is very old

_____ — a daily record

_____ — one who leads others

_____ — a bird of the barn-door or poultry kind

_____ — an odd or fantastic action or trick

_____ — a place where milk is kept, and butter and cheese made

_____ — one who watches over and protects others

_____ — the thick, soft fine hair of certain animals

_____ — an unfair attack which breaks the rules of a game

B Here are ten more nouns.

ballet	cereal	gaol	lair	quire
ballot	choir	goal	layer	serial

Write each of these nouns in front of its meaning, as given here.

_____ — a quantity of paper, usually twenty-four sheets

_____ — a food prepared from grain, especially a breakfast food

_____ — a secret vote marked on a ticket or paper and put into a box

_____ — a chorus or band of singers

_____ — a prison or jail

_____ — a substance spread evenly over another

_____ — a performance of graceful dancing and action to music

_____ — a story or a play in instalments

_____ — the den or hiding-place of a wild beast

_____ — in football, the space marked by two upright posts and a crossbar

Reading from the record

A At a country school, children living on farms were asked to record what animals were reared or what crops were grown on their farms.

The record looked like this. Each child put a tick ✓ to show what was on the farm.

	Cows	Sheep	Pigs	Corn	Poultry
Alex	✓	✓		✓	
Beth	✓		✓		✓
Carly		✓		✓	✓
David			✓		✓
Elliot	✓	✓			

From this record, answer these questions.

1 Who has cows but no poultry?_____.

2 Who has sheep but no corn? _____.

3 Who has pigs but no cows? _____.

4 Who has both cows and poultry? _____.

5 Who has both sheep and corn?_____.

6 Who has both pigs and cows?_____.

7 Who has poultry but no cows?_____.

8 Who has corn but no cows?_____.

9 Who has poultry but no sheep? _____.

10 Who, do you think, lives on the smallest farm?_____.

B Anford, Belton, Carstone, Darbridge, Exton and Faymouth are six towns.

Darbridge and Faymouth have two cinemas each. The others have only one each.
All except Belton have a park.
All except Carstone and Exton have a river.
Belton, Darbridge and Exton have a station. The others have not.
Carstone and Faymouth have markets. The others have not.

From the details given above, fill in this record of the six towns.

	Cinemas	Park	River	Station	Market
Anford					
Belton					
Carstone					
Darbridge					
Exton					
Faymouth					

From the record you have just completed, answer these questions.

1 Which town has neither a station nor a market? _____

2 Which town has neither a river nor a station? _____

3 Which town has neither a river nor a market? _____

4 Which town has two cinemas but no market? _____

5 Which town has a park, a river and a station? _____

6 In which town do you think the second cinema is near the market? _____

A helping hand

Dad is building a wall. His family and neighbours are helping by carrying bricks from the pile to the place where he is working.
They carry the same number each time. All the bricks are the same weight.

By counting the bricks each one carries, answer these questions:

1   Who is carrying **most** bricks? _____

2   Who is carrying **fewest** bricks? _____

3   Who is carrying **more** bricks than Ann? _____

4   Who is carrying **fewer** bricks than Larry? _____

5   Who is carrying **more** bricks than Larry? _____

6   Who is carrying **fewer** bricks than Mum? _____

7   Who is carrying the **heaviest** load? _____

8   Who is carrying the **lightest** load? _____

9   Who has a **lighter** load than Larry? _____

10   Who has a **heavier** load than Mum? _____

11   Who says, "I am carrying **fewer** than my Dad but **more** than you, Ann."?

_____

12   Who says, "If you gave me your bricks, Ann, I would then have **the same number**

as Larry's Dad."? _____

13   After a time Dad says, "I only need ten more, now."

Write out three ways in which some of the five people, working together in one trip, could bring Dad exactly ten bricks.

a _____   **b** _____

c _____

14   Make up your own question using the names of Mum and Jessica, to which the answer must be 'Ann'.

_____

_____

Apostrophe 's

When we write about someone's possessions, we put **'s** after their name.

For example, This is Jac**k's** house.   That is Da**d's** car.

Here is Mu**m's** shopping basket.   I have borrowed Bery**l's** bicycle.

A Write the name with its apostrophe **'s** in each of these sentences.

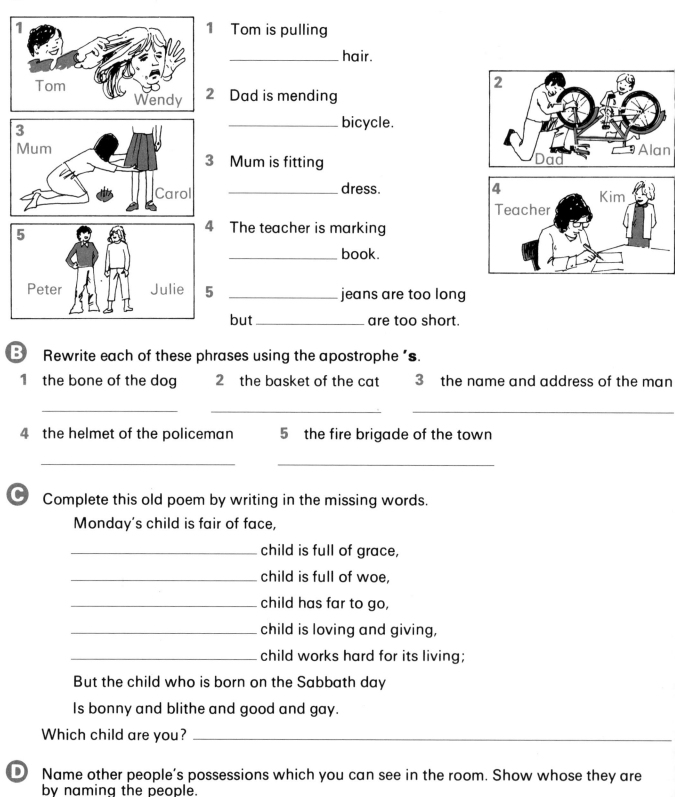

1 Tom is pulling

_____ hair.

2 Dad is mending

_____ bicycle.

3 Mum is fitting

_____ dress.

4 The teacher is marking

_____ book.

5 _____ jeans are too long

but _____ are too short.

B Rewrite each of these phrases using the apostrophe **'s**.

1 the bone of the dog   **2** the basket of the cat   **3** the name and address of the man

_____   _____   _____

4 the helmet of the policeman   **5** the fire brigade of the town

_____   _____

C Complete this old poem by writing in the missing words.

Monday's child is fair of face,

_____ child is full of grace,

_____ child is full of woe,

_____ child has far to go,

_____ child is loving and giving,

_____ child works hard for its living;

But the child who is born on the Sabbath day

Is bonny and blithe and good and gay.

Which child are you? _____

D Name other people's possessions which you can see in the room. Show whose they are by naming the people.

_____

_____

Opposites

In the list of phrases below there is an **adjective** with a **noun**.
After each phrase write another phrase which means exactly the opposite.
Choose an **adjective** from **Panel A** and a **noun** from **Panel B**.
When you have used a word from either panel, put a tick ✓ after it.
The first one is done for you.

Panel A	Panel B
bad ✓	announcement
cheap	answer
clear	attic
cowardly	copy
dark	defeat
dry	departure
dull	descent
early	enemy ✓
easy	evening
few	exit
last	exports
low	exterior
miserable	fall
past	finish
peaceful	lining
plain	loss
poor	peace
possible	pigmy
public	quietness
quick	refusal
rude	retreat
short	scowl
sudden	summer
tiny	valley
warm	villain

1   a good friend _____ *a bad enemy* _____
2   a difficult climb _____
3   an enormous giant _____
4   a courageous hero _____
5   a slow advance _____
6   a late arrival _____
7   an exciting start _____
8   a happy smile _____
9   a long war _____
10 a disturbing noise _____
11 a well-lit entrance _____
12 a polite acceptance _____
13 a cool cellar _____
14 a luxurious interior _____
15 a first rise _____
16 a valuable invention _____
17 a wet winter _____
18 an impossible question _____
19 a cloudy morning _____
20 numerous imports _____
21 a private secret _____
22 a steady gain _____
23 a decorated cover _____
24 a future victory _____
25 a high mountain _____

The vanishing herds of Uganda

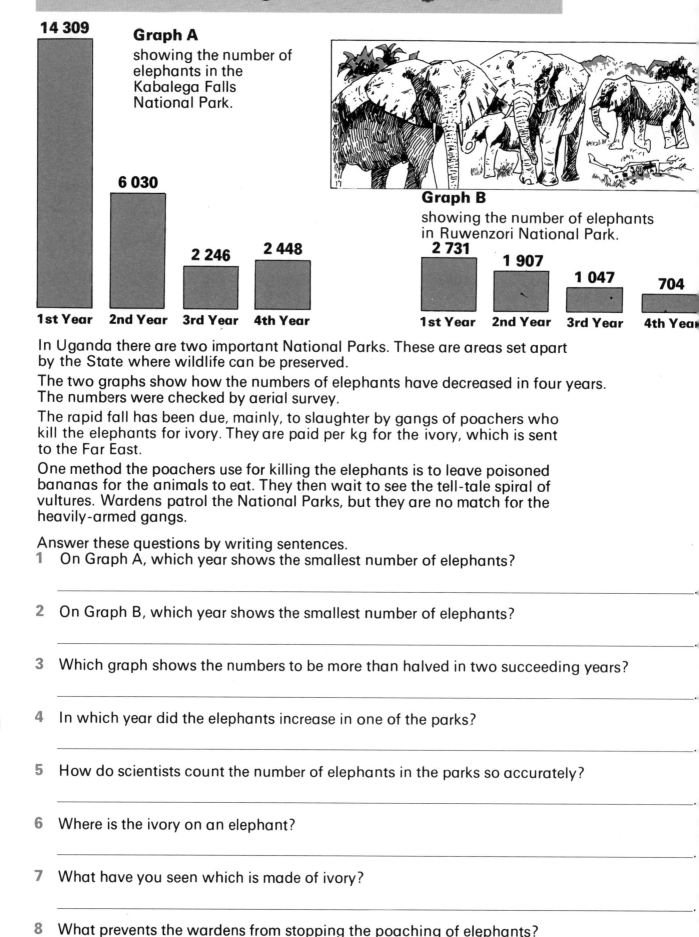

14 309

Graph A
showing the number of elephants in the Kabalega Falls National Park.

6 030

2 246 **2 448**

1st Year 2nd Year 3rd Year 4th Year

Graph B
showing the number of elephants in Ruwenzori National Park.

2 731

1 907

1 047

704

1st Year 2nd Year 3rd Year 4th Year

In Uganda there are two important National Parks. These are areas set apart by the State where wildlife can be preserved.

The two graphs show how the numbers of elephants have decreased in four years. The numbers were checked by aerial survey.

The rapid fall has been due, mainly, to slaughter by gangs of poachers who kill the elephants for ivory. They are paid per kg for the ivory, which is sent to the Far East.

One method the poachers use for killing the elephants is to leave poisoned bananas for the animals to eat. They then wait to see the tell-tale spiral of vultures. Wardens patrol the National Parks, but they are no match for the heavily-armed gangs.

Answer these questions by writing sentences.

1 On Graph A, which year shows the smallest number of elephants?

_____

2 On Graph B, which year shows the smallest number of elephants?

_____

3 Which graph shows the numbers to be more than halved in two succeeding years?

_____

4 In which year did the elephants increase in one of the parks?

_____

5 How do scientists count the number of elephants in the parks so accurately?

_____

6 Where is the ivory on an elephant?

_____

7 What have you seen which is made of ivory?

_____

8 What prevents the wardens from stopping the poaching of elephants?

_____

9

continuously curved line   disappearing   became fewer

mass killing   way

From this list of words and phrases, choose the correct one to write as the meaning of each of these words.

a   vanishing _____   **b**   slaughter _____

c   method   _____   **d**   decreased _____

e   spiral   _____

10   What **bait** is used by the elephant poachers?

_____

11   This report is about the African elephant. What other type of elephant is there, and how does it differ from the African elephant?

_____

12

carrion   flocks   greedy   prey   victims

flesh   grasping   large   ugly   waiting

Using any of the words from this list, write sentences describing a **vulture**.

_____

_____

_____

_____

_____

_____

13

central   continent   country

inland   north

Using the words in this list, and from details on the map, write sentences to answer the question, "Where is Uganda"?

_____

_____

_____

_____

14   If you were in charge of the two National Parks, what would you do to save the elephants?

_____

_____

_____

Last to first

In this exercise, the **last four** letters of one word are the **first four** letters of the second word.

For example,

b	r	e	a	d	→	r	e	a	d	i	n	g

c	u	s	t	o	m	→	s	t	o	m	a	c	h

In each of the following, complete each word by writing a letter in each square.

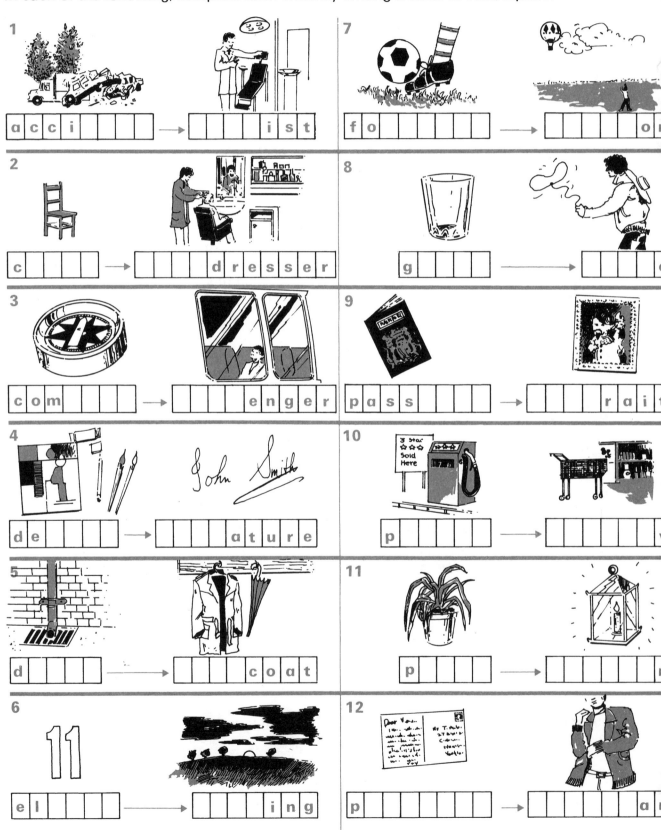

1
| a | c | c | i | | | | → | | | | | i | s | t |

2
| c | | | | | → | | | | d | r | e | s | s | e | r |

3
| c | o | m | | | | → | | | | e | n | g | e | r |

4
| d | e | | | | | → | | | | a | t | u | r | e |

5
| d | | | | | → | | | | c | o | a | t |

6
| e | l | | | | | → | | | | i | n | g |

7
| f | o | | | | → | | | | | o | r |

8
| g | | | | | → | | | | o |

9
| p | a | s | s | | | → | | | | r | a | i | t |

10
| p | | | | | → | | | | | |

11
| p | | | | | → | | | | | r |

12
| p | | | | | | → | | | | | a | r |

Page 28

Last to first—*continued*

Following the same rule as on page 28, complete each of these words.

13 `s` `h` □ □ □ → □ □ □ □ □ `y`

14 `s` □ □ □ `g` → □ □ □ □ □ □ □ `e` `r`

15 `s` □ □ □ □ → □ □ □ □ `d`

16 `s` □ □ □ □ → □ □ □ □ □ `g`

17 `s` `p` □ □ □ → □ □ □ □ `r`

18 `s` `p` □ □ □ → □ □ □ □

19 `s` □ □ □ □ → □ □ □ □ `m`

20 `t` □ □ □ □ □ □ → □ □ □ `y`

21 1000 → `t` □ □ □ □ □ □ → □ □ □ □ □ □ `h`

22 `t` □ □ □ □ □ → □ □ □ □ `t`

23 `t` □ □ □ □ → □ □ □ □ `w`

24
Brighter weather will spread from the west. Winds light to moderate, freshening. Outlook—warmer· 15°C
`f` □ □ □ □ □ □ □ → □ □ □ □ `e`

25 NOT GUILTY — WORDS FROM A TO Z — `v` □ □ □ □ □ → □ □ □ □ □ □ □ `y`

26 `p` □ □ □ □ → □ □ □ □ □ `d`

Verbs—present tense and past tense

A In each of these exercises the verbs in the first sentence are **in the present**. Write the verbs in the second sentence **in the past**. The first one is done for you.

1 Our dog **barks** and then **begs** for something.

This morning it ___*barked*___ and then ___*begged*___ for its bone.

2 As the new day breaks the farmer begins his work.

As the new day _____ the farmer _____ his work.

3 Every time Tom blows his nose vigorously it bleeds.

Last week he _____ it and it _____ for ten minutes.

4 The osprey breeds in Scotland and builds its nest in a tree.

For nearly fifty years it was thought no ospreys _____ in Britain,

and they certainly _____ no nests.

5 At the monthly auction sale Grandpa usually bids for something and often buys a trinket.

Last month he _____ for and _____ a set of medals.

B In each of these exercises the verbs in the first sentence are **in the past**. Write the verbs in the second sentence **in the present**.

1 In the last match the cricketer **batted** sixth.

He usually _____ first.

2 The dry wood burst into flames and burnt away quickly.

The drier it is the quicker it _____ into flames and the quicker

it _____ away.

3 Yesterday, our dog, Bruno, bit the man who brought the parcel.

He _____ anyone who _____ anything to the house.

4 When a squire became a knight he bore arms for his king.

When a squire _____ a knight he _____ arms for his king.

5 The cooper bent and bound the iron hoops around the cask.

A cooper _____ and _____ iron hoops around casks.

Commentating and reporting

Verbs—present tense and past tense

A commentator talks about an event as **it is happening** in the **present** tense.
A reporter writes about an event after **it has happened**, in the **past** tense.

For example,

"The cars **are lining** up on the starting-grid. The noise of their engines **swells** up into a roar. The starter **raises** his flag. As it **falls**, the champion **is** away first."

The verbs he uses are all in the **present**.

The cars **lined** up on the starting-grid. The noise of their engines **swelled** up into a roar. The starter **raised** his flag. As it **fell** the champion **was** away first.

The verbs he uses are all in the **past**.

(A) Read what this commentator is saying. He uses verbs in the present.
Write out the reporter's account, using verbs in the past.

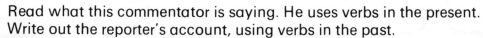

"Hundreds of people **are** still pouring into the stadium as the referee **blows** his whistle for the start of the game. The burly Jim Smith **kicks** off and the wave of white shirts **surges** towards goal. The move **breaks** up when red-shirted Wayne Gibbs **throws** himself forward and **heads** the ball down. His partner **runs** free of his opponent and **centres** into the goalmouth where the goalie **catches** the ball and **throws** it out of the danger area."

_____
_____
_____
_____
_____
_____
_____

(B) This commentator is describing a fashion show. She uses verbs in the present.
Write out the reporter's account, using verbs in the past.

"As the sound of soft music **drifts** through the room, we **see** that the model, Karen, **is** wearing a turquoise dress. She **walks** gracefully to the end of the platform where she **stops**, **turns** and **pauses**. She **holds** out the folds of the dress and we **notice** the sheen on the material, which **gives** added glamour to the outfit. She **is** wearing a matching hat and **carries** a handbag and gloves of the same colour."

_____
_____
_____
_____
_____
_____

Name the instruments

By each picture, write a sentence including its name from **Panel A** and its use from **Panel B**.

Panel A	Panel B
barometer	magnifies small things
compass	used for listening to the heart and lungs
compasses	used for drawing circles
microscope	measures pressure of the atmosphere
pressure gauge	measures air pressure in a tyre
protractor	used for finding directions
set square	when struck, gives a sound of known pitch
speedometer	used for drawing, or checking, lines at right angles
stethoscope	shows the speed of a vehicle
tuning-fork	used for measuring angles on paper

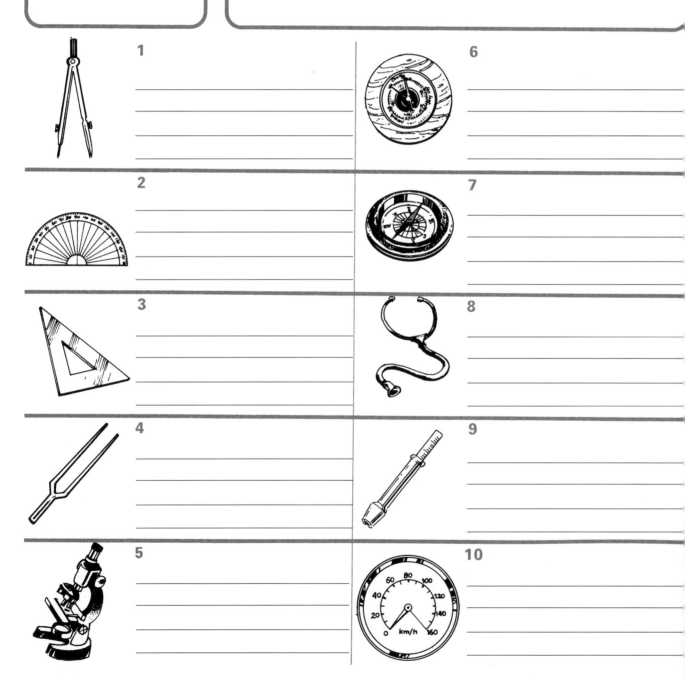

1

2

3

4

5

6

7

8

9

10

Name the instruments

By each picture, write a sentence including the name of the instrument from the list below to describe what it is used for.

corkscrew	magnet	spirit-level	telephone	thermometer
hearing-aid	microphone	syringe	telescope	tin-opener

1 _____
_____
_____
_____

5 _____
_____
_____
_____

2 _____
_____
_____
_____

6 _____
_____
_____
_____

3 _____
_____
_____
_____

7 _____
_____
_____
_____

4 _____
_____
_____
_____

8 _____
_____
_____
_____

9 _____
_____
_____

10 _____
_____
_____

Correct order

These numbers are in **mixed order**   four,   ten,   two,   eight,   six.
In **correct order**, starting with the **lowest**, they are   two,   four,   six,   eight,   ten.

These are in **mixed order**   month,   century,   week,   year,   fortnight.
In **correct order**, starting with the **smallest**, they are   week,   fortnight,   month,   year, century.

A   Starting with the **lowest**, write the words in each of these groups in correct order.

1   three,   one,   five,   two,   four

2   eleven,   fifteen,   nine,   seven,   thirteen

3   fifteen,   five,   twenty-five,   ten,   twenty

4   trunk,   leaf,   root,   twig,   branch

5   legs,   head,   waist,   feet,   shoulders

6   walls,   spire,   foundations,   weather-vane,   roof

7   ground floor,   attic,   basement,   first floor

8   hillside,   coastline,   sky,   sea-level,   mountain peak

B   Starting with the **smallest**, write the words in each of these groups in correct order.

1   minute,   day,   hour,   week,   second

2   village,   city,   hamlet,   town,   cottage

3   word,   book,   letter,   line,   page

4   single,   half,   double,   quarter,   treble

5   sleeve,   jacket,   cuff,   suit,   button

6   duet,   quartet,   choir,   trio,   soloist

7   river,   spring,   ocean,   stream,   sea

8   few,   many,   all,   none,   some

Odd one out

In each of these groups of five words, one word is the **odd one out**.
In some way it differs from the other four.

For example, **witch, sorcerer, clown, magician, wizard**

clown is the odd one out because the other four all deal in magic.

Find the odd one out in each group, and write it in the space at the end of the line.

1   cabin,   hut,   garden,   shack,   shed   _____

2   baker,   butcher,   farmer,   florist,   greengrocer   _____

3   avenue,   road,   street,   track,   signpost   _____

4   guard,   spy,   warden,   sentry,   watchman   _____

5   bellow,   howl,   roar,   speak,   yell   _____

6   always,   century,   day,   month,   year   _____

7   blanket,   carpet,   eiderdown,   pillow,   sheet   _____

8   customer,   dealer,   merchant,   shopkeeper,   trader   _____

9   hard,   harsh,   sad,   stern,   strict   _____

10 battery,   glow-worm,   lamp,   lantern,   torch   _____

11 fall,   hit,   knock,   punch,   tap   _____

12 log,   fuel,   plank,   splinter,   stick   _____

13 barn,   bungalow,   cottage,   house,   mansion   _____

14 bed,   cradle,   crib,   hammock,   table   _____

15 companion,   comrade,   friend,   mate,   neighbour   _____

16 neat,   pretty,   smart,   tidy,   trim   _____

17 famous,   genuine,   real,   sincere,   true   _____

18 attach,   bind,   fasten,   join,   sever   _____

19 clue,   mystery,   problem,   puzzle,   riddle   _____

20 blank,   empty,   hollow,   roomy,   vacant   _____

21 enlarge,   extend,   finish,   increase,   lengthen   _____

22 bread,   cake,   milk,   pancake,   pastry   _____

23 blind,   curtain,   screen,   shutter,   window   _____

24 arrange,   grade,   order,   mix,   sort   _____

25 cold,   damp,   moist,   soaking,   wet   _____

The Lombard R.A.C. Rally

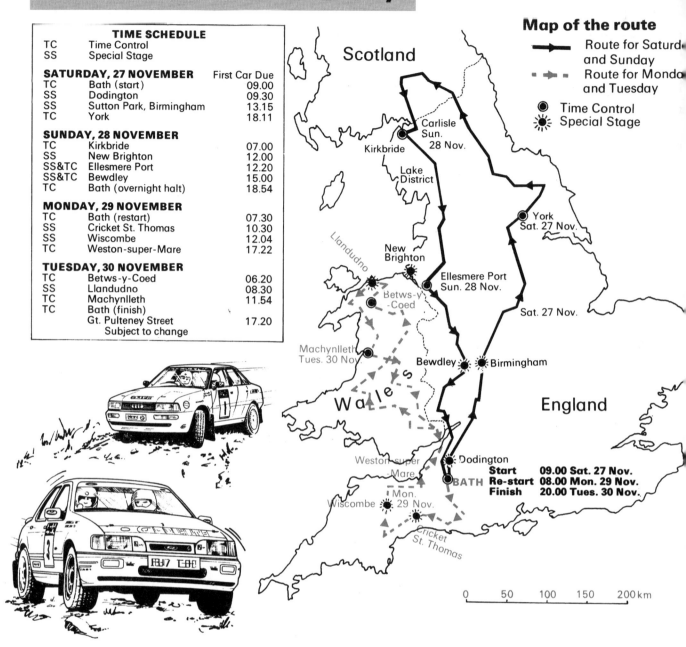

TIME SCHEDULE

TC	Time Control	
SS	Special Stage	

SATURDAY, 27 NOVEMBER — First Car Due

TC	Bath (start)	09.00
SS	Dodington	09.30
SS	Sutton Park, Birmingham	13.15
TC	York	18.11

SUNDAY, 28 NOVEMBER

TC	Kirkbride	07.00
SS	New Brighton	12.00
SS&TC	Ellesmere Port	12.20
SS&TC	Bewdley	15.00
TC	Bath (overnight halt)	18.54

MONDAY, 29 NOVEMBER

TC	Bath (restart)	07.30
SS	Cricket St. Thomas	10.30
SS	Wiscombe	12.04
TC	Weston-super-Mare	17.22

TUESDAY, 30 NOVEMBER

TC	Betws-y-Coed	06.20
SS	Llandudno	08.30
TC	Machynlleth	11.54
TC	Bath (finish)	
	Gt. Pulteney Street	17.20
	Subject to change	

Map of the route

→ Route for Saturday and Sunday

- ➤ - Route for Monday and Tuesday

◉ Time Control

☀ Special Stage

Start 09.00 Sat. 27 Nov.
Re-start 08.00 Mon. 29 Nov.
Finish 20.00 Tues. 30 Nov.

The rally spans four days with only one overnight stop at Bath. Two hundred crews, many of them professionals, will take part supported by service teams to carry out repairs en route. Each car has to be specially prepared beforehand, and it has to be made stronger than the normal car. It is expected that a total of two million spectators will watch the rally. Of the seventy-five Special Stages only two dozen have been advertised, in order to keep down the number of sightseers at possible danger spots. Over five thousand marshals along the route will check the drivers' times. This is most important on the Special Stages which are held on private roads or forest tracks, where there are no traffic laws. The winner will be the one who has taken the shortest time over the whole four days of fast and skilful driving.

Answer these questions by writing sentences.

1 What do the letters R.A.C. mean? _____

2 The route covers over 3000 km in three countries. Which countries are they?

_____

3 In which town will the crews sleep for one night?

4 Each crew consists of two people. One drives. What does the other one do?

5 Why could there be danger spots for spectators at some places?

6 Why must the cars be strongly built?

7 What kind of emergencies must the service team be prepared for?

8 How many Special Stages are kept secret from the public?

9 Which word in the extract means the same as **spectators**?

0

| beginner | expert | novice | amateur | learner |

Which of these words is the opposite of **professional**?

11 Where have you read of a **marshal** before?

12 A diary for the year of the rally says

   "SATURDAY 27 NOVEMBER   s.r. 07.38 hours   s.s. 15.57 hours."

On that day, between which two places on the map will the cars have their headlights switched on?

13 Of which of these traffic offences are drivers likely to be guilty on the private roads or forest tracks?

being an unaccompanied L-driver   giving no clear hand-signals
driving dangerously   having no driving-licence
exceeding the speed limit   not keeping to the left-hand side
                                                        of the road

14 Apart from the thrills for the crews and spectators, what good do you think the rally does?

Words with augh or ough

A Read aloud these words.

although	brought	dough	laughed	plough	thorough
borough	caught	draught	laughter	rough	thought
bough	cough	enough	nought	slaughter	through
bought	daughter	fought	ought	taught	tough

B Write each word in its correct rhyming panel.

This rhymes with **off**

_____

These rhyme with **sought**

_____
_____
_____
_____
_____
_____

These rhyme with **now**

_____
_____

These rhyme with **water**

_____
_____

These rhyme with **toe**

_____
_____

This rhymes with **rafter**

_____

These rhyme with **muff**

_____
_____

These rhyme with **raft**

_____
_____

This rhymes with **two**

_____

This rhymes with **borough**

_____

C Complete each of these sentences by writing words chosen from the list.

1 Once harvest is over, the farmer begins to _____ his fields.

2 The man escaped over the prison wall but he was soon _____.

3 Everyone _____ at the clown when he fell _____ the trapdoor.

4 The baker had just _____ _____ to make a small loaf.

5 Julie has a bad cold and _____, probably because she has been sitting in a _____.

6 Daren _____ all his pocket - money to the jumble sale and _____ the toy spaceship he had always wanted.

7 The boys _____ that the _____ of the tree was strong _____ to carry their swing.

8 The street has a very _____ surface and it has a notice which says, "No _____ road".

9 The boxing match was _____ at great speed, and it was clear that the champion had a _____ opponent.

10 Mr. Johnson, who has _____ at this school for over ten years, is to be the next mayor of the _____.

Book covers and book titles

A

Air Routes of the World
The Art of Ballet Dancing
Tales of Ferndale Farm
Robin Hood and his Merry Men

Thirty Years with the Big Top
The Secret Garden
The Sea keeps its Secrets
With Richard on the Crusades

Choose the most suitable to write on each of these book covers.

B

Make up and write your own titles for these two book covers.

Remember, titles must have capital letters.

Books of all kinds

an atlas	a dictionary	a gazetteer	The Koran
The Bible	a diary	a guidebook	a log-book
a catalogue	an encyclopaedia	a handbook	a year-book

A From the list, choose the correct name to write in front of these descriptions.

1 _____ contains the Christian scriptures.

2 _____ records the performance of a ship or aircraft, and events on its journey.

3 _____ contains the Muhammadan scriptures.

4 _____ gives a complete list of items, usually in alphabetical order or in groups, and often with details and price.

5 _____ is a book of maps or charts.

6 _____ contains words in alphabetical order, together with their meanings.

7 _____ gives information on all kinds of knowledge, or on one special subject, and is usually arranged alphabetically.

8 _____ gives information about a place or district which is useful to a tourist.

9 _____ lists the events and records of the past year.

10 _____ is a book in which to make daily records or to note engagements.

11 _____ is an index of geographical names and words.

12 _____ is a manual which usually contains hints or instructions.

B After each of these items, write the name of the book in which it appears.

1 "17.15 hours —sighted land to NE—changed course to NNW." _____

2 "WALES and the MIDLANDS   Scale 1:1 000 000." _____

3 "A bird's wings are large and powerful. They are pushed down hard enough to lift its body off the ground. The muscles which move them (see Fig. 23) are the largest in the body." _____

4 "zodiac—belt of the heavens divided by the ancients into twelve equal parts called signs." _____

5 "Visit the fourteenth-century church. See stained glass windows and Norman font." _____

6 "6.30 p.m.—dress rehearsal for school play." _____

7 "Mediterranean Sea—separates Europe from Africa." _____

8 "April 22—Over one million people have attended Liverpool's games at Anfield this season." _____

9 "Shed, cedar— 2m by 2m—apex roof—£89·50." _____

10 "Every 10 000 km check the hand-brake mechanism." _____

11 "Muhammad is the father of no man among you. He is the Messenger of Allah and the seal of the prophets." _____

12 "When Jesus saw the multitudes, he was moved with compassion toward them." _____

Stories from words

ere are five words in mixed order.   sleeping   tanned   beach   sun   chair

alphabetical order they are   **beach   chair   sleeping   sun   tanned**

hese sentences use the words in their alphabetical order.

We were able to spend most of our holiday on the **beach**. For much of the time Dad was in his **chair**, forgetting his worries and **sleeping**. The **sun** shone every day, and we returned home looking **tanned** and fit.

A Write each group of words in alphabetical order.

B Write sentences using the words in alphabetical order.

puncture   walk   bicycle   tyre   journey

_____

_____

_____

_____

_____

2 dream   thousands   festival   woke up   pop star

_____

_____

_____

_____

3 trick   circus   whitewash   tripped   clowns

_____

_____

_____

_____

4 day   sports   competitor   winner   jumping

_____

_____

_____

_____

5 hurricane   overboard   wreckage   boat   leaking

_____

_____

_____

_____

Word meanings

Some words have more than one meaning.

For example, **arms** can mean  or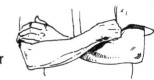

Write the correct word, which has a double meaning, for each of these pictures.

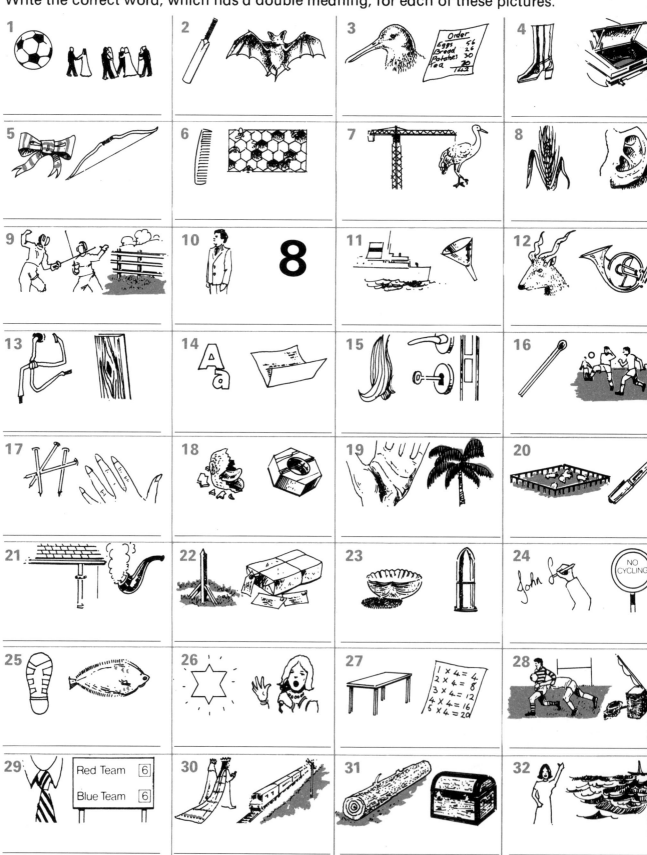

Nouns with the same meaning

Choose a word from **Column B** and a word from **Column C** to write after each word
Column A to make a group of three nouns which have the same meaning.

Put a tick ✓ after each chosen word. The first group is done for you.

Column A

1	astonishment	_amazement_	_surprise_
2	battle		
3	cellar		
4	danger		
5	edge		
6	force		
7	guard		
8	howl		
9	incident		
10	joy		
11	knock		
12	labour		
13	merchant		
14	nonsense		
15	order		
16	path		
17	quest		
18	region		
19	scent		
20	test		
21	umpire		
22	valour		
23	worry		
24	yarn		

Column B	Column C
amazement ✓	absurdity
area	anxiety
blow	basement
border	bravery
command	contest
courage	cry
defender	dealer
fight	district
foolishness	event
happening	examination
judge	expedition
peril	happiness
pleasure	instruction
route	menace
search	perfume
smell	power
strength	protector
tale	rap
trader	referee
trouble	rim
trial	story
vault	surprise ✓
work	toil
yell	track

Names

A The **English** are natives of **England**, the **Irish** are natives of **Ireland**, the **Scots** are natives of **Scotland** and the **Welsh** are natives of **Wales**.

1 After each of these names of the inhabitants, write the name of their native country.

Belgians _____	Chinese _____	Danes _____
Dutch _____	French _____	Germans _____
Greeks _____	Israelis _____	Mexicans _____
Norwegians _____	Poles _____	Spaniards _____
Swedes _____	Swiss _____	Turks _____

2 What is the name of your country? _____

B A Brummie comes from Birmingham, a Bristolian comes from Bristol and a Cantabrigian comes from Cambridge.

1 After each of these, write the names of the city where each of these people come from.

an Aberdonian _____	a Cockney _____
a Glaswegian _____	a Liverpudlian _____
a Mancunian _____	an Oxonian _____

2 What name, based on where you live, is given to you? _____

C Some countries or counties have given their names to some food or dish.

1 After each of these names, write the name of the food or dish which is well-known.

Cornish _____	Irish _____	Lancashire _____
Scotch _____	Welsh _____	Yorkshire _____

2 Describe one of the six dishes above. _____

_____

D Some places and some people have given their names to everyday objects.

For example, Canterbury in Kent—Canterbury Bell, a garden flower.
　　　　　　　J. Léotard—leotard, a one-piece garment worn by ballet-dancers.

After each of these names, describe the object which has been called after it. A clue is given in brackets.

1 Axminster, in Devon—(for the home) — _____

2 Louis Braille—(for reading) — _____

3 Brussels, in Belgium—(for eating) — _____

4 Earl of Cardigan —(for wearing) — _____

5 Earl of Derby —(for horses) — _____

6 R. Diesel—(for power) — _____

7 G. D. Fahrenheit—(for measuring) — _____

8 C. Macintosh—(for wearing) — _____

9 Sam F. B. Morse—(for messages) — _____

10 Duke of Wellington—(for wearing) — _____

Twenty creatures

The names of many creatures have double letters in them.

For example, bu**ff**alo, gira**ff**e, gori**ll**a, mi**nn**ow, sh**ee**p.

Here are twenty, all of which have double letters.

Write the name of each creature in the end column. The first letter of the name is given.

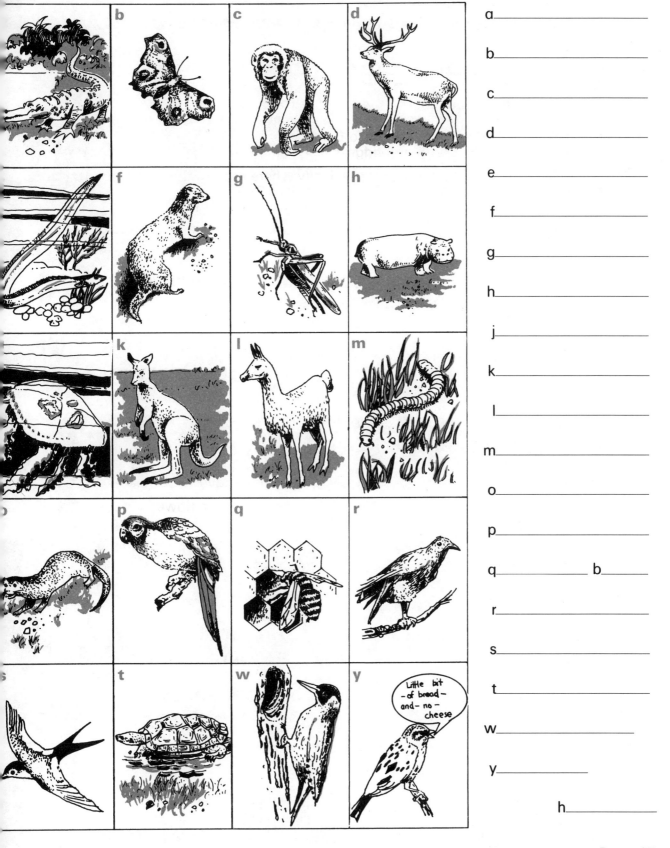

a_____

b_____

c_____

d_____

e_____

f_____

g_____

h_____

j_____

k_____

l_____

m_____

o_____

p_____

q_____ b_____

r_____

s_____

t_____

w_____

y_____

h_____

Schofield & Sims
HELPING CHILDREN TO LEARN

Schofield & Sims was established in 1901 by two headmasters and since then our name has been synonymous with educationally sound texts and teaching materials. Our mission is to publish products which are:

- **Educationally sound • Good value • Written by experienced teachers**
- **Extensively used in schools, nurseries and play groups**
- **Used by parents to support their children's learning**

SPRINGBOARD 7

Nine English workbooks providing a wide range and progressive programme of language exercises. The series covers word construction, comprehension exercises, spelling, creative work and vocabulary.

Springboard Introductory Book - 0 7217 0883 8

Springboard Book 1 - 0 7217 0884 6

Springboard Book 2 - 0 7217 0885 4

Springboard Book 3 - 0 7217 0886 2

Springboard Book 4 - 0 7217 0887 0

Springboard Book 5 - 0 7217 0888 9

Springboard Book 6 - 0 7217 0889 7

Springboard Book 7 - 0 7217 0890 0

Springboard Book 8 - 0 7217 0891 9

Schofield & Sims Key Stage 2 products for 7 to 11 year olds

Language and literacy workbooks
Key Spellings
Books 1 - 4
Pattern and sound based spelling activities and exercises to establish basic spelling skills.

New Spellaway
Books 1 - 4
A progressive series complementing the formal teaching of spelling. New patterns are consolidated, through the 'look, say, cover, write, check approach'.

Posters
Sturdy laminated posters, full colour, write-on/wipe-off, suitable for wall mounting or desk top use. Over 70 titles covering numeracy, literacy, science, nature, geography, history and languages.

Maths and numeracy workbooks
Times Tables
Books 1 and 2
Straight forward tables practice.
Book 2 covers x6, x7, x8, x9, x11, x12 tables
(Book 1 is for Key Stage 1)

Mental Arithmetic
Books 1 - 6 plus Introductory Book
Covers essential mental maths skills through 36 carefully graded tests in each book along with progress tests and diagnostic tests. Supported by a corresponding series of Teacher's Books.

Schofield & Sims

Dogley Mill, Fenay Bridge, Huddersfield, HD8 0NQ
Phone 01484 607080   Fax 01484 606815

e-mail sales@schofieldandsims.co.uk

Information
For further information about products for pre-school, Key Stages 1 and 2, please request our catalogue or visit our website at
www.schofieldandsims.co.uk

ISBN 0-7217-0890-0

9 780721 708904

Price £1.95
Key Stage 2
Age Range 7-11 years